Over in the Meadow

A Counting Rhyme

Introduction

One of the best ways you can help
your children learn and learn to read
is to share books with them. Here's why:

• They get to know the **sounds**, **rhythms** and **words**
used in the way we write. This is different from how we
talk, so hearing stories helps children learn how to read.

• They think about the **feelings** of the characters
in the book. This helps them as they go about
their own lives with other people.

• They think about the **ideas** in the book. This helps
them to understand the world.

• Sharing books and listening to what your children
say about them shows your children that you care
about them, you care about what they think
and who they are.

Michael Rosen

Michael Rosen
Writer and Poet
Children's Laureate (2007-9)

For Gran
Margaret Craig
McDougall

First published 1994 by Walker Books Ltd
87 Vauxhall Walk, London SE11 5HJ

This edition published 2011

2 4 6 8 10 9 7 5 3 1

Illustrations © 1994 Louise Voce
Concluding notes © CLPE 2011

This book has been typeset in Baskerville

Printed in China

British Library Cataloguing in Publication Data:
a catalogue record for this book is available from the British Library

ISBN 978-1-4063-3512-5

www.walker.co.uk

Over in the
Meadow

A Counting Rhyme

Illustrated by Louise Voce

WALKER BOOKS

AND SUBSIDIARIES

LONDON · BOSTON · SYDNEY · AUCKLAND

Over
in the meadow

in the sand

in the sun ...

Lived an old mother turtle
and her little turtle
ONE.
"Dig," said his mother.
"I dig," said the One;
So he dug all day
in the sand in the sun.

Over in the meadow
where the stream runs blue,
Lived an old mother duck
and her little ducklings
TWO.
"Quack," said their mother.
"We quack," said the Two;
So they quacked all day
where the stream runs blue.

Over in the meadow
in a hole in a tree,
Lived an old mother owl
and her little owls
THREE.
"To-whoo," said their mother.
"To-whoo," said the Three;
So they to-whooed all day
in a hole in a tree.

Over in the meadow
by the big barn door,
Lived an old mother mouse
and her little mice
FOUR.
"Squeak," said their mother.
"We squeak," said the Four;
So they squeaked all day
by the big barn door.

Over in the meadow
in a snug beehive,
Lived an old mother bee
and her little bees
FIVE.
"Buzz," said their mother.
"We buzz," said the Five;
So they buzzed all day
round their snug beehive.

Over in the meadow
in a nest built of sticks,
Lived an old mother squirrel
and her little squirrels
SIX.
"Jump," said their mother.
"We jump," said the Six;
So they jumped all day
round their nest built of sticks.

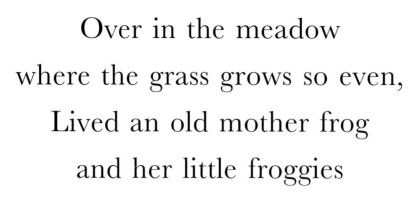

Over in the meadow
where the grass grows so even,
Lived an old mother frog
and her little froggies
SEVEN.
"Hop!" said their mother.
"We hop!" said the Seven;
So they hopped all day
where the grass grows so even.

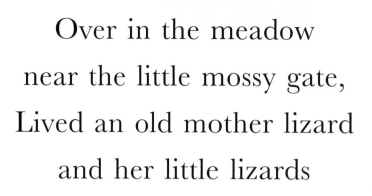

Over in the meadow
near the little mossy gate,
Lived an old mother lizard
and her little lizards
EIGHT.
"Run," said their mother.
"We run," said the Eight;
So they ran all day
on the little mossy gate.

Over in the meadow
by the tall Scots pine,
Lived an old mother pig
and her little piglets
NINE.
"Oink!" said their mother.
"We oink," said the Nine;
So they oinked all day
near the tall Scots pine.

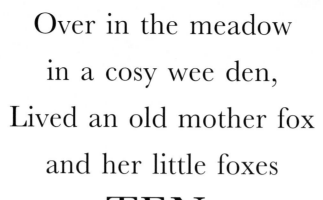

Over in the meadow
in a cosy wee den,
Lived an old mother fox
and her little foxes
TEN.
"Play," said their mother.
"We play," said the Ten;
So they played all day
round their cosy wee den.

Over in the meadow
in the sand in the sun...

1   digs

2   quack

3   to-whoo

4   squeak

5   buzz

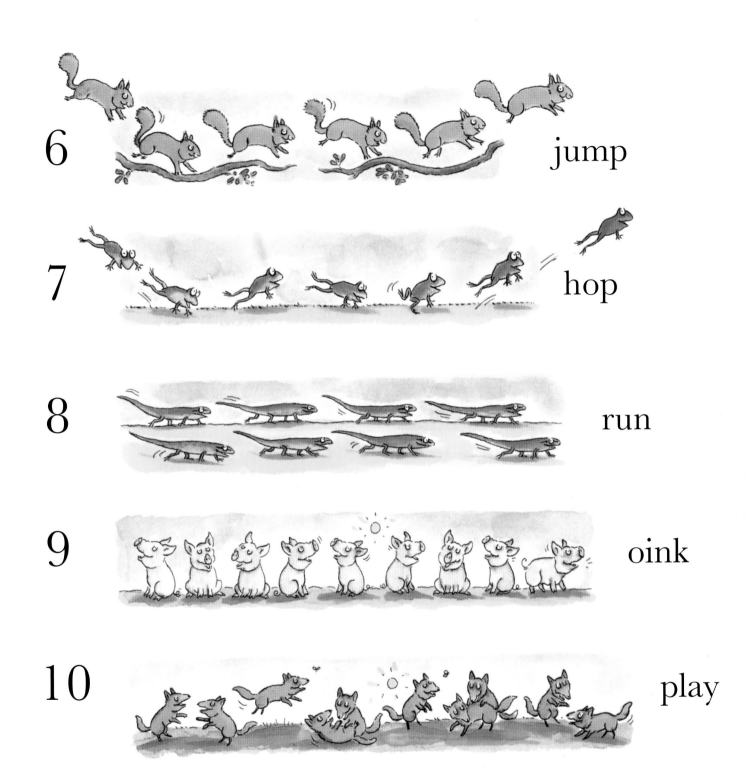

6   jump

7   hop

8   run

9   oink

10   play

over in the meadow
till the end of the day.

Sharing Stories

Sharing stories together is a pleasurable way to help children learn to read and enjoy books. Reading stories aloud and encouraging children to talk about the pictures and join in with parts of the story they know well are good ways to build their interest in books. They will want to share their favourite books again and again. This is an important part of becoming a successful reader.

Over in the Meadow is a picture-book version of a traditional counting rhyme. It offers strong support to young readers through rhyme, rhythm and song. Here are some ways you can share this book:

• Encourage children to join in with the story whenever they can, making the animal noises and movements, or counting the animals.

• You can use the rhymes and pictures to help children to guess the rhyming words. Encourage them to join in by leaving spaces for them to finish the rhyme. It's fun and helps them to listen to the sounds and rhythms of the story.

• By hearing the book sung aloud again and again, children will get to know it almost word for word. Don't worry if they say it in their own way.

• Knowing the song by heart will help them to begin matching the words they sing with those on the page.

• Read and sing other counting rhymes and songs together, using actions to add to the shared enjoyment.

SHARE A STORY
A First Reading Programme
From Pre-school to School

Beginnings – 2 years+

Look Out, Suzy Goose — Petr Horáček — Introduced by Michael Rosen

Walking Through the Jungle — Julie Lacome — Introduced by Michael Rosen

Hello, Goodbye — David Lloyd, Louise Voce — Introduced by Michael Rosen

Ten in the Bed — Penny Dale — Introduced by Michael Rosen

This is the Bear — Sarah Hayes, Helen Craig — Introduced by Michael Rosen

The Big Wide-Mouthed Frog — Ana Martín Larrañaga — Introduced by Michael Rosen

Early Steps – 3 years+

A New House for Mouse — Petr Horáček — Introduced by Michael Rosen

The Train Ride — June Crebbin, Stephen Lambert — Introduced by Michael Rosen

The Other Day I Met a Bear — Russell Ayto — Introduced by Michael Rosen

Old MacDonald Had a Farm — Jane Chapman — Introduced by Michael Rosen

The Tiger and the Jackal — Vivian French, Alison Bartlett — Introduced by Michael Rosen

Zed's Bread — Mick Manning, Brita Granström — Introduced by Michael Rosen

Next Steps – 4 years+

The Hairy Toe — Daniel Postgate — Introduced by Michael Rosen

The True Story of Humpty Dumpty — Sarah Hayes, Charlotte Voake — Introduced by Michael Rosen

Beans on Toast — Paul Dowling — Introduced by Michael Rosen

Over in the Meadow — A Counting Rhyme — Louise Voce — Introduced by Michael Rosen

Dog Blue — Polly Dunbar — Introduced by Michael Rosen

Night-night, Knight And Other Poems — Michael Rosen, Sue Heap — Introduced by Michael Rosen

Taking Off – 5 years+

"Have You Seen the Crocodile?" — Colin West — Introduced by Michael Rosen

Handa's Surprise — Eileen Browne — Introduced by Michael Rosen

The Ravenous Beast — Niamh Sharkey — Introduced by Michael Rosen

One, Two, Flea! — Allan Ahlberg, Colin McNaughton — Introduced by Michael Rosen

Dinosaurs' Day Out — Nick Sharratt

The Old Woman and the Red Pumpkin — Betsy Bang, Rachel Merriman — Introduced by Michael Rosen

Sharing the best books makes the best readers

WALKER BOOKS

www.walker.co.uk